'JESUS HEALS'

(EIGHT LETTERS TO FRIENDS)

by

Barbara Lightowler

MOORLEY'S Print & Publishing

ISBN 0 86071 406 3

MOORLEY'S Print & Publishing

23 PARK ROAD, ILKESTON, DERBYS., DE7 5DA · ENGLAND

CONTENTS

'THE MAN WITH THE PARALYSED HAND'

Dear John,

I fear for Jesus and I feel that it is all my fault. If he had not healed me on the Sabbath I'm sure none of this would have happened.

How grateful I am to be cured. You do not know what it feels like to have no use in a hand. No-one wanted to employ me. Who wants to give work to someone with only one hand when there are so many with two good hands looking for jobs?

But, if I had known how the Pharisees were going to turn against Jesus like they have, I would have forgone my cure. Jesus does not deserve this. He works for the people, healing, forgiving and helping them.

You were not there in the synagogue when Jesus had his brush with them, were you?

People seemed to be in an ugly mood. They were looking for ways of accusing Jesus of doing wrong. *'Is it against our Law to heal on the Sabbath?'* they asked of him.

Jesus thought for a moment then asked them, if one of their sheep fell down a ravine on the Sabbath, would they leave it there to rot or would they take hold of it and pull it out? Everyone looked uncomfortable because they knew the answer was to rescue the sheep, whatever day it was.

Jesus nodded his head. *'And a man is worth much more than a sheep,'* he said. *'So then, our Law does allow us to help someone on the Sabbath.'*

Then he looked at me. I was quivering with excitement and a sense of dread at what was being said. *'Stretch out your hand'*, he told me. I lifted it and straightened out the fingers. I lifted my other hand, stretching them both together and there was no difference between them. I clenched my fists and stretched out my fingers again. I turned round and picked up the Bible which was lying on the table and I gently turned over the pages with my new hand.

I was not too full of my joy, however, not to notice the rage in the Pharisees. They had murder in their eyes as they left the synagogue.

What can we do to help Jesus, John? Tell me and I will do anything for him.

I wait to hear from you.

Levi.

(Accounts of this miracle can be found in the Gospels of Matthew, ch. 12:9-14, Mark ch. 3:1-6 and Luke ch. 6:6-11.)

'THE WOMAN WHO TOUCHED HIS CLOAK'

My Dear Sarah,

I just had to write to you with my joyful news. I am cured. Yes, cured. After all these years, twelve long, painful years, I am cured.

You do not believe me, do you? After the way I have written to you for such a long time, pouring out my troubles, I do not blame you.

You, my dear friend, who never failed to cheer me with your loving and caring words, are the first to know my wonderful news.

It happened only yesterday.

You must have heard of Jesus, you know, the one who has been so much in the news lately. The one who gathers the crowds around him. Well, he was having a meeting in our village and somehow, even though I could barely put one foot before the other, I felt that I must go. I must see and hear this man. It was a compulsion.

I went.

Oh what a joy to hear his gentle voice. The crowds milled around him almost obscuring him from my view.

"I wish I could get nearer to him", I murmured, more to myself than to anyone else.

You can. A voice inside me seemed to urge me on. So I pushed my way through the throng.

Suddenly he was there right in front of me; but his back was towards me. If only I could touch his cloak, I thought. Just caress it with the tip of one finger I know that I will be healed.

I bent low and skimmed the fringe with my hand.

And Sarah, you will not believe this but, as if he had heard my thoughts, he turned. *"Who touched my cloak?"* he asked. Those wonderful eyes looked right into mine and gently he smiled.

The ones who help him, the ones they call the disciples, stared at Jesus. *"There must be hundreds of people touching you, Lord, in this crush"*, one of them said. Jesus just smiled again and his eyes never left mine.

There was a hush in the crowd as he said, *"Take heart, daughter."* He called me daughter and me old enough to be his mother. *"Take heart, daughter, your faith has healed you and made you well."*

And it is true! I am well! Cured and full of love for Him.

Soon I will be able to visit you. I am so looking forward to seeing you.

Your loving friend,

Naomi.

(Accounts of this miracle can be found in the Gospels of Matthew, ch. 9: 20-22, Mark ch. 5: 25-34 and Luke ch. 8: 43-48.)

'THE ROMAN OFFICER'S SERVANT'

My Dearest wife, Claudia,

I write to you because I must tell someone what has happened here in Capernaum today.

I cannot speak of it to my fellow officers, but, as it is so incredible, no doubt they will hear of it from some source or other, so I do not know what will happen to me because of it.

Forgive me for going on so but I can hardly believe it happened myself.

You, my dearest, loving wife, know me better than anyone and I know you will understand why I turned to this Jesus as I did.

Have you heard of this man, Jesus? You may not know of him in Rome, yet. He seems to have done most of his work here in the Lake Galilee area.

We sometimes have trouble with the crowds who follow him. It's quite frightening really. Thousands flock round him and you know what the Governor thinks of allowing the Jews to gather in crowds. He's very much against it so we have to go in and split them up. You can imagine what happens then. Cursing. Shouting. Fighting. Riots. And we have to sort it all out.

Anyway, my dear, enough of all that. It is not why I am writing to you at all. But it does give you the reasons why I cannot talk to other Romans about what happened.

You know that I am a caring person. I like everyone to be happy and that includes those who work for me. This is why they remain loyal and have served under me for years. I do not like to see them suffer so when one of my faithful servants became dreadfully ill yesterday I didn't know what to do.

He was so ill that he could not be moved and there were no physicians willing to take a look at him. Then another servant whispered in my ear that there was a man called Jesus coming into town that day and he cured people, even brought them back to life.

Of course I thought him to be quite deranged and did not believe a word he had said but, as there was no other solution, I went to meet this Jesus.

As he walked towards me a strange thing happened. I felt quite light-headed and my heart quickened. There was something so different about this man that I just knew he had the authority to heal my servant.

I told him that the poor man was too ill to move and that he was at my house a mile or so away.

"I will go and make him well", he said. I was quite taken aback. He was willing to go all that way to my house to heal my servant and I was not even of his faith or culture.

I shook my head, "No, Sir", I said. "You give the order and my servant will be well. I too serve under superior officers and I have many soldiers under me. If I say to one do this or that, it is done. I know that if you say that my servant is healed he will be just that."

Jesus seemed surprised but he heard me out then turned to those who followed him and told them that he had never found anyone in Israel who had a faith like mine. It gave me quite a shock to hear him say that. He then said to me: "Go home, and what you believe will be done for you."

I rushed back to the house to be met by my servant at the door and, when we compared the times, discovered that he had begun to feel better at the exact moment Jesus had spoken to me.

Now you can see why I cannot speak to my fellow Romans about this.

Since meeting this Jesus I know that my life will never be quite the same again.

I long to have my leave so that I can come home to Rome to see you and talk about this great feeling inside me.

Don't be afraid, my dearest, and do not talk of these things to anyone else until I see you.

I remain your loving and devoted husband.

Saul.

(Accounts of this miracle can be found in the Gospels of Matthew ch. 8: 5-13 and Luke ch. 7:1-10.)

'THE BLIND MEN'

Dear Simeon,

How are you? Isn't it wonderful that we are now able to see? What a day it was last week when Jesus healed us.

I can't get over all the colours around me. The blue sky, the brown of God's earth and the purple and red of the bougainvillea. Sometimes the sheer brilliance of it hurts my eyes and I have to close them to give them a rest. It is just wonderful.

Do you feel the same?

My most glorious moment was when I looked at my children. I have never seen them before. They are all so different from what I had pictured. My wife looked older, but still as beautiful as the day I married her. It is just ten years since I last saw her face.

And we have Jesus to thank for it all.

I thought, when he went into the house without turning round at our calls, that he either had not heard us or was not going to acknowledge us. *"Take pity on us, Son of David"*, we had called, and he kept on walking in front of us. My heart was heavy at that point.

I'm so glad you persuaded me to go into the house with you. You have always been such a good friend to me, Simeon, You were the only person who understood when I realised my sight was deteriorating. Of course, you have been blind so much longer than I; you were the right one for me to turn to. I'm glad we were able to face Jesus together.

What did you really feel when Jesus asked us if we believed that he could heal us?

My heart, which had been so down a few moments before, suddenly soared to the heavens and I just knew - really knew that he could heal us, that God really was within him.

And when he touched my eyes, well, I can't describe the feeling. It was like a raging heat; yet his fingers were cool, gentle.

As for asking us not to tell anyone. Well, really! As if we could keep something like that secret! I couldn't wait to tell everyone I met.

And everyone should know what a healer Jesus is. What miracles he makes happen. I've heard many tales of others he has cured. The lame are made to walk again and demons are sent packing.

We must count ourselves as richly blessed and give thanks to God for our sight.

I look forward to seeing you soon - how good it is to actual mean that!

Jeremiah.

(The account of this miracle can be found in the Gospel of Matthew ch. 9: 27-31.)

———————————

'THE MAN WITH DEMONS'

Dear Friends at Gerasa,

You used to know me as 'Mob' because of the demons which once possessed me. I am so sorry for the way I have behaved these many moons and hope that you will believe me when I tell you that the situation was quite out of my own hands, and will forgive me.

It is so good to be alive again. Yes, alive, for that is how it feels since Jesus drove out those monsters from within me. I feel born again.

In great trepidation I visited the caves yesterday and can hardly believe that I once dwelt there amongst those burial mounds and rocks. I found the chains which once bound me and do not know where I got the strength to break them like I did.

I owe my new life to Jesus and was so sad when you drove him away. I know that you were terribly afraid of what happened but Jesus is a good man. He is gentle and kind and I will be eternally grateful to him for what he has done for me.

Of course I am sorry too for the herdsmen who lost their pigs. They will have told you all about the horror of it. There were so many demons inside me that when they entered the herd, of many hundreds, they sent them completely wild and they rushed down the hillside and were drowned in the lake.

Some of you saw me soon afterwards and can vouch that I am now really cured.

I wanted to go with Jesus, to be one of his many followers, but he asked me to return home to my family and friends and tell you all about what has happened. That is why I am writing to you today. I will be visiting you all very soon, then you can see for yourselves that I am healed, that it is not merely a temporary thing.

Jesus truly is the Son of God. Only God could do such things that have been done to me.

Although quite afraid and apprehensive at first, and who can blame them for that - my family are now so happy to have me back. I can work once again and I will do all in my power to repay those who lost their herd.

My life has taken on a new meaning and I praise God for each new day.

I am once again your friend,

Joshua the Potter.

(Accounts of this miracle can be found in the Gospels of Mark ch 5: 1-20; Luke ch. 8: 26-39 and Matthew ch. 8: 28-34 although in Matthew's account he tells of two men with demons.)

_____

'THE DUMB MAN'

Dear Philip,

I have followed Jesus for so long now. Because I could not speak I used to sit and watch and listen. I never wanted to go home. I could have listened to him forever.

Because I could not speak I kept to the back of the crowd, just near enough to hear what was being said. I never dreamt of going to Jesus and asking him to cure me. I was content to listen and watch.

Glory seemed to shine from him.

I remember one day as he stood on the hill and we all sat down on the grass no-one wanted to go home. Jesus fed us on a little boy's lunch of loaves and fishes. Somehow he shared that little bit of food between us all. I don't know how he did it. But I sat and watched and listened.

Then, as you know, things changed for me. You all persuaded me to let Jesus help me. I had been so busy watching him healing others and marvelling at it; but, I can truly say, I had never once considered that he could do anything for me. You, Philip, and my other friends talked me into going to see Jesus and I will be for ever grateful to you.

The 'thing' which was inside me and had prevented me from speaking for so long was cast out and, immediately, as you know, I began to speak.

Forgive me for going over it all again, you must be tired of hearing me relate it to everyone, let alone putting it down in writing to you! But I am so overcome with joy and gratitude that it is difficult for me to think and speak of anything else.

It upset and angered me, though, to hear the Pharisees

talking amongst themselves after Jesus had healed me. They spoke of his power coming from the devil rather than God.

Talk like that is very dangerous and I wondered if you could go to see them. You have such a way with words, I've always admired you. Tell them that Jesus is a good man and that his healing power really does come from God. I would go myself but I do not feel confident enough yet. Speech is very new to me. I would not be able to find the right words.

Please, Philip, will you do this for me and for our friendship?

I remain your true friend,

Matthew.

(The account of this miracle can be found in the Gospel of Matthew ch. 9: 32-34.)

'THE MAN WITH SKIN DISEASE'

Dear Ahab,

Yes, it's me, your old friend, Joel. Please, don't be afraid. Don't drop the paper and start scrubbing your hands. Is that what you did? I don't blame you. You do right to take precautions against this dreaded disease. But now there is no need. You see, Joel, I am cured for ever.

"I do not believe it", you're saying. Am I right? Yes, I thought so. And I too would have been very doubtful until today. After all, the physicians told me that I would never get better from it. No-one gets better from such a disease.

But, today, I met a man called Jesus. Do you know of him? I had heard talk about him. *"He cures all ills,"* people said.

Cures all ills, Ahab. There couldn't be a worse ill than this cursed skin trouble which has almost turned me into an animal, foraging for scraps not fit even for the dogs. Turned me into a hermit. Lost. Alone. Many times I wished for death to come quickly to me. God, forgive me for such thoughts.

But, no more such wishes. I want to live. I want to go back to my beloved work. To fashion those lengths of cloth. To mix my dyes and weave the yarns.

And yes, Ahab, I can do it now that Jesus came into my life. Let me tell you how it happened. Although he told me not to tell anyone I just cannot keep something like this to myself. So I write to you, my oldest friend, knowing that you will keep my secret.

I have visited the priest, as Jesus asked me to do, he examined me and, although he could hardly believe it himself, he could do no other than pronounce me cured. I offered my sacrifice, as Moses taught us, then sat straight down to write this letter to you.

Large crowds follow Jesus wherever he goes and today was no exception. Of course, I could not go in amongst the people, they would stone and kick me. Then Jesus went up a hill and sat down. His special helpers, I have heard them called disciples, followed him and stopped the people from crowding too close.

The voice of Jesus could be heard and he seemed to be teaching these men, telling them to be merciful and kind to others and to work for peace in the world.

I was overcome with the beauty of his voice and the authority in it. I edged as near as I dare.

After some time Jesus came down from the hill, and although people crowded in on him, I suddenly saw a space, there, right in front of him. I knelt down before him and he stopped and looked at me. *"Sir"*, I said. *"Please make me clean. I know you can do it if you want to."*

Jesus stretched out his hand and he touched me. The feeling was like a shock wave going through my body. *"I do want to"*, he said. *"Be clean."*

I looked down at my hands, I felt my face. I drew up my clothes and gazed at my legs. Even my feet, those crippled toes; everything was clean and smooth and healed.

I felt the tears pouring down my cheeks. The people who, on my approach, had all stepped back away from me in their fear, suddenly cheered and clapped. Some came and patted me on the back. What a feeling that was, Ahab. No-one has touched me for over a year.

I so much look forward to seeing you and your family once again. I never thought that I would see the day when that would be possible.

Until we meet I remain your true and good friend,

Joel.

(Accounts of this miracle can be found in the Gospels of Matthew ch. 8: 1-4; Mark ch. 1: 40-45 and Luke ch. 5: 12-16.)

'THE PARALYSED MAN'

Dear Sarah,

You didn't expect to hear from me again after the accident I had with the handcart, did you? I don't remember much about it really, I think I must have passed out with the pain. What I do remember is opening my eyes and seeing the tears pouring down your cheeks. I tried to lift my hand to hold yours but found I could not move. I couldn't even feel your fingers as they stroked my arm.

There was no future for us then. As Joshua and John lifted my paralysed body onto a mat and carried me home I knew that I might never see your lovely face again. Marriage to you now was out of the question. We had such plans too. But I realised that you would have to find someone else to share your life, someone able to work and help bring up a family.

You may have already heard, of course - news about Jesus seems to travel fast. Do you know that I am now healed from the paralysis? It is true! A miracle!

Joshua and John and the others heard that Jesus was back in Capernaum and carried me on my mat to see if I could be healed by him. You must have heard about the things he has been doing. Well, when we got there the place was so crowded. There were Pharisees and teachers of the Law there from all over Galilee and Judaea and even from Jerusalem. We had no chance of getting my bed into the house. No-one was willing to let us through.

It was John's idea that we go up on the roof. They wound some twine around me so that I would not slip from the mat. Then, very carefully, they managed to get me up the steps. Then, as quietly as possible, they began to tear off the roof covering to make a hole big enough to lower me through. I can smile about it now, we must have looked quite idiotic, trying such a thing. At the time, though, it was all quite serious and feverish.

With the aid of the twine my friends lowered me to the ground, right at the feet of Jesus. I can tell you, everyone was quite amazed.

Jesus looked up at my helpers and, seeing how much faith they had, he smiled and lifted his hand to them in greeting. Then he gazed down at me. *"Your sins are forgiven, my friend"*, he said.

Now that really caused a stir. The Pharisees and the teachers didn't like that at all. I could hear them muttering about blasphemy. I became quite afraid for Jesus.

"God is the only one who can forgive sins", they murmured. Jesus seemed to know what they were thinking and turned to them.

"Which is easiest, to say your sins are forgiven or to say to this man, get up and walk?" Everyone stared at Jesus. *"I will prove to you that the Son of Man has authority here on earth to forgive sins."*

There was a hush and I held my breath. Then, Sarah, he turned to me and told me to get up, pick up my bed and walk. Suddenly feelings and energy surged through my body and I rolled off my mat onto my knees, stood up, bent down to pick up my bed and went home.

My friends chased after me cheering and we all praised God. We got down on our knees, there in the middle of the road, and offered our thanks and songs to God. People were staring at us and laughing, no doubt they thought we were drunk or mad. And we were, in a way, drunk with the joy of living and mad with love for Jesus.

I will now come to the main reason I write to you, Sarah. You have probably already guessed. If you are still free and want me, please will you be my wife? Joshua will be delivering this for me, please give him your answer.
I am yours in God.

Simon.

(Accounts of this miracle can be found in the Gospels of Luke ch. 5: 17-26, Mark ch. 2: 1-12 and Matthew ch. 9: 1-8.)

MOORLEY'S ... are growing Publishers, adding several new titles to our list each year. We also undertake private publications and commissioned works.

Our range of publications includes: **Books of Verse**
Devotional Poetry
Recitations
Drama
Bible Plays
Sketches
Nativity Plays
Passiontide Plays
Easter Plays
Demonstrations
Resource Books
Assembly Material
Songs & Musicals
Children's Addresses
Prayers & Graces
Daily Readings
Books for Speakers
Activity Books
Quizzes
Puzzles
Painting Books
Daily Readings
Church Stationery
Notice Books
Cradle Rolls
Hymn Board Numbers

Please send a S.A.E. (approx 9" x 6") for the current catalogue or consult your local Christian Bookshop who should stock or be able to order our titles.